Eureka!

—Great Discoveries and Achievements in Science, Engineering, and Technology—

世界を飛躍させた偉人たち

—英語で学ぶ理工系の常識—

NAN'UN-DO

Eureka!

—Great Discoveries and Achievements in Science, Engineering, and Technology—

Philip Zamrej Graham
Gordon A. Reid
Takeo Tanaka
Chikako Sawada
Mikinari Matsuoka
Naofumi Okumura

Download Audio

音声ファイル
無料 DL
のご案内

このテキストの音声を無料で視聴（ストリーミング）・ダウンロード
できます。自習用音声としてご活用ください。
以下のサイトにアクセスしてテキスト番号で検索してください。

https://nanun-do.com　テキスト番号［**511963**］

※無線 LAN（WiFi）に接続してのご利用を推奨いたします。

※音声ダウンロードは Zip ファイルでの提供になります。
お使いの機器によっては別途ソフトウェア（アプリケーション）
の導入が必要となります。

はじめに

◆本書の目的や特徴について

本書は、これまで世界で活躍してきた偉人たちのエピソードを紹介しながら、学生の皆さんが、英語のテキストを楽しんで理解することができるよう執筆したものです。大学生の皆さん、とくに、工学部の学生の皆さんが、工学関連分野における偉人たちに関する英文を通し、英語の総合的な運用能力を高めていくことを目的として、各エピソードの偉人たちの発明に関する説明部分には、工学的な要素を含めました。古代から現代にわたる歴史上有名な発明家に関するエピソードは、どれも興味をもって読んでいただけるものと思います。

◆各ユニットの構成について

本書は、15 のユニットから構成されており、1 つのユニットは次のような構成になっています。Pre-Reading では、各ユニットで紹介される偉人やその偉人が発明したものに関する背景知識を尋ねる質問をもとに、英語でやりとりしながら本文を読む動機を高めるように作られています。Reading text では、偉人やその偉人が発明したものについてのエピソードが、500 語程度の比較的平易な英語で書かれています。通常の英語テキストには、難しいと思われる語句に訳注などが付けられていますが、本書では大学生の皆さんが自ら考えリサーチする力を身に付けることも目標のひとつとし、敢えて訳注などは付けませんでした。Vocabulary は、英文テキスト中に出てきた重要語句の意味理解を確認する問題です。Understanding 1&2 は、それぞれ英文テキストの内容を確認する問題になっています。Understanding 1 は、概要をつかむための選択肢問題となっており Understanding 2 は、詳細な内容を捉えるための真偽問題として作成されています。

Dictation では、英文テキストで取り上げた偉人や発明に関するプラスアルファの情報を英語で聞いて空所を埋めるディクテーション問題になっています。Think About It は、英文テキストで取り上げた発明について工学的な部分のみを取り出した英語での要約になっています。英語での解説をまずは理解し、それをイラストで描写し自分なりの英語でイラストを表現してみるという応用問題となっています。巻末には、各ユニットで扱ったトピックについて英語でディスカッションできるような Further ‘Think About It’ Questions を用意しています。さらに活動が必要な場合、ご使用していただければと思います。

◆さいごに

本書をきっかけにして、英語に対する興味をもっていただき、英語力をさらに向上させる一助に本書がなることを執筆者一同、心より願っています。

2020 年 2 月　執筆者一同

Contents

Unit 1 Archimedes (c.287-c.212B.C.)

Archimedes

Pre-Reading

Answer the following questions with a partner:

1) Do you know the story of Archimedes and the golden crown?
2) Can you complete the following formula: $\text{Density} = \frac{\text{Mass}}{?}$
3) Which metal is denser, gold or silver?
4) If you had a piece of gold and a piece of silver the same weight, which piece would be bigger?
5) Which has the greater volume, a kilogram of rocks or a kilogram of feathers?

Reading text

02

The English word 'polymath' actually comes from two Greek words: '*poly*' and '*math*', which mean '*much*' and '*learn*'. In modern English, it means a person who has lots of knowledge of many different subjects. So, polymath is definitely a word that could be used to describe Archimedes. A mathematician, physicist, engineer, inventor and astronomer, this remarkable man lived in the city of Syracuse in modern Sicily from c.287 – c.212 BC.

Maybe you have heard the story about Archimedes lying in the bathtub one day thinking about a tricky problem. On suddenly realizing the solution, he is said to have jumped up and cried, 'Eureka!' (I have found it!). It is said that he was so excited that he ran through the streets naked!

What had Archimedes 'found', however? Well, have you ever wondered why very large ships don't just sink in the ocean? The answer is to be found in Archimedes' principle. This states that:

The buoyant force on a submerged object is equal to the weight of the fluid that is displaced by the object.

In other words, if you put an object in water, some of the water is displaced. Simultaneously, the force of buoyancy pushes up on the object; this alters its weight in the water. If the object weighs more than the amount of water, it will sink. If, however, the displaced water is equal to the weight of the object, it will float. The heavier an object is, the more water it needs to displace, which is why big boats have large, hollow hulls. The wide hulls displace more water, while being hollow keeps the weight down.

So, Archimedes' principle explains why large, heavy ships can float, but what problem was he trying to solve that day while lying in the bath? You may have heard the story of Archimedes and the golden crown. Hiero, the king of Syracuse, had asked a goldsmith to make him a new golden crown. The king was very pleased with the magnificent crown that the goldsmith produced, but soon he began to hear rumours that he may have been tricked. It was said that the goldsmith had replaced some of the gold with an equal amount of silver. King Hiero decided to ask Archimedes if he could find some way of determining whether the crown was pure gold.

Archimedes knew that gold was denser than silver, so a piece of gold weighing the same amount as a piece of silver would be smaller. Therefore, a gold and silver crown would have a greater total volume than a pure gold crown. The problem was how to measure the volume of an irregular shaped object, which Archimedes figured out in his 'Eureka' moment.

He lowered a piece of pure gold, which was the same weight as the crown, into a pot filled with water and measured the amount of water that spilled out. He then did the same thing with the crown. The crown displaced more water than the piece of gold, proving that it had been mixed with silver. Hiero had his answer and the goldsmith was punished.

Archimedes was killed in c.212 during a battle for the city of Syracuse. As well as his work with water, he is remembered for many other inventions and theories, and was truly one of the world's great engineers.

MEMO

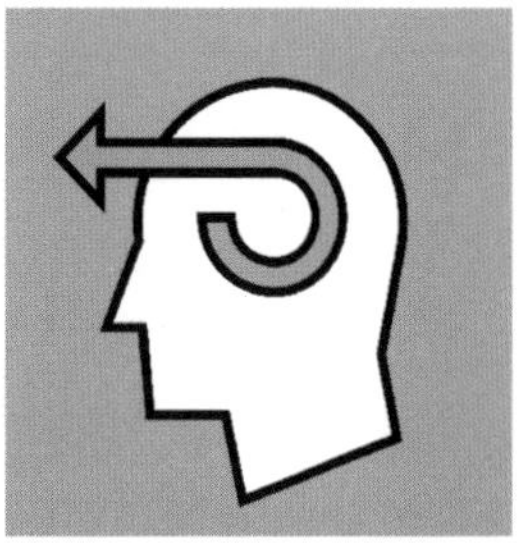

Vocabulary

The underlined word appears in the text. Choose the word below which best matches the underlined word.

1) Inventors often need to think long and hard to solve tricky problems.
   a) difficult b) impossible c) trivial

2) After a submarine dives, it is completely submerged in the water.
   a) under b) alone c) immersed

3) The hull of the Titanic struck an iceberg, causing it to sink.
   a) main body b) crew c) deck

4) Engineers sometimes have to determine the strength of various metals.
   a) change b) establish c) improve

5) Metals can be melted and then crafted into all kinds of irregular shapes.
   a) unbelievable b) standard c) variable

Understanding 1

Look at the reading passage and choose the correct expression.

1) As a polymath, Archimedes was interested in many different -------.
   a) people b) subjects c) places

2) When Archimedes figured out the -------, he was so excited that he forgot to get dressed.
   a) reason b) solution c) time

3) As water is moved by an object, something called buoyancy ------- acts against the submerged object.
   a) in opposition b) conversely c) simultaneously

4) Various people suggested that some gold in the crown had been r______________ by silver.

5) When Archimedes lowered the crown into water, it ______________ a greater amount of water than it should have done.

Understanding 2

Look at the reading passage again and decide if the following statements are true or false. Be ready to explain your choice.

1) T / F If an object displaces water equal to its weight, it will float.

2) T / F Big boats have large, hollow hulls to make them lighter.

3) T / F King Hiero believed at once that the goldsmith had tricked him.

4) T / F Two lumps of gold and silver that are the same weight will be different sizes.

5) T / F Because the crown was not pure gold, it displaced more water than if it had been pure gold.

Dictation

03

Listen and fill in the blanks using the words below:

accurate	lower	dense	astronomer	peace
swapped	sink	believed	denser	astronaut
piece	scales	pure	low	accept

The famous Italian mathematician and 1. ______________, Galileo Galilei, was interested in Archimedes' problem with the crown. Galileo 2. ______________ that lowering a crown and a 3. ______________ of gold into water would not be 4. ______________ enough to determine that the crown was not 5. ______________ gold. Instead, he believed that Archimedes would have used a set of 6. ______________, with the crown on one side and a piece of gold on the other. In this test, the 7. ______________ object with the smaller volume for the same weight would sink 8. ______________ in the water. Therefore, the lump of pure gold would 9. ______________ more than the crown, proving that the goldsmith had 10. ______________ some gold for silver.

Think about it

Below is an explanation of how you could prove Archimedes' principle with a simple experiment. With a partner, or in a small group, make a diagram to illustrate the experiment. Be ready to explain your diagram in English!

Fill a beaker that has an overflow spout with water until the water comes out of the spout. When water stops flowing out of the spout, the water level in the beaker will now be level with the spout. Take an object, a stone or piece of wood, for example. Weigh the object on a hanging scale, and note the weight. Next, put an empty beaker on a standard scale, such as would be used for cooking, and place them both directly under the spout. Reset the standard scale to zero. Lower the object, still attached to the hanging scale, into the beaker of water so that the object is completely submerged. Displaced water will flow out of the spout into the empty beaker. When the flow stops, check the weight on the standard scale, and note it down. The weight of the object in the air minus the weight of the object in the water will be equal to the weight of the displaced water. This represents the buoyant force on the object, and proves Archimedes' principle.

Go to page 98 for a further activity.

Unit 2 Leonardo da Vinci (1452-1519)

Leonardo da Vinci

Pre-Reading

Answer the following questions with a partner:

1) Have you ever flown in an airplane? Where did you go?
2) What is the most famous painting you have ever seen?
3) How can human beings fly without the help of an engine?
4) Tell your partner what you know about Leonardo da Vinci.
5) If you could be an inventor, what would you like to create?

Reading text

04

Ever since humans first saw birds in the sky, people have dreamed of soaring above the clouds. Of course, nowadays we can get on an airplane and fly around the world, but in the 15th century, this was just a dream. One man, however, tried very hard to make this dream a reality.

Leonardo da Vinci is someone that most of you will probably have heard of. His painting 'Mona Lisa' is in all likelihood the best-known piece of art in the world. This remarkable man was born in 1452 in the Republic of Florence, now part of modern-day Italy. He was, and still is, widely considered to be one of the most diversely talented individuals ever to have lived. One of the many challenges that Leonardo da Vinci set himself was to create a flying machine. Indeed, he is sometimes credited with inventing the airplane, helicopter and parachute, some 500 years before their time.

Leonardo made many hundreds of sketches on the subject of flight, often buying birds at the local market in order to study their wings. He believed that a method for human flight could be found in the natural world, particularly in bats and birds. Bats seemed to have been one of his main inspirations, and in many of his sketches, the wings resemble bat wings.

An ornithopter is a flying machine that mimics a bird and is powered by a human, and Leonardo designed one that he hoped would fly. It had a wingspan of roughly 10 metres, and it was made principally from pine and silk. In this device, the pilot would lie face down on a board and use his legs to pedal a crank, which was connected to a rod and pulley system. There was also a steering device, and a hand crank to provide extra power. It is not known for sure whether Leonardo da Vinci ever tested his device, but while it may have flown when airborne, it would have been impossible for it to get off the ground using human power alone.

Although the ornithopter was probably always destined to remain on the ground, Leonardo's designs for a glider were more practical. Detailed in his Codex on the Flight of Birds, 1505, his glider design included the idea that the pilot could control the machine by shifting body weight. This was an idea used over 350 years later by glider pioneers in the late 19th century. Leonardo also understood the way in which gliding birds balanced themselves with both their wings and tail. When the Wright brothers were creating their first aeronautical designs, they would also utilize this knowledge.

Leonardo died in 1519, having never left the ground. However, his aeronautical designs and ideas on flight were both groundbreaking and an inspiration to future designers and inventors.

MEMO

Vocabulary

The underlined word appears in the text. Choose the word below which best matches the underlined word.

1) There have been many remarkable people throughout history.
   a) old b) extraordinary c) unusual

2) It is said that people sometimes resemble their pet dogs.
   a) look like b) dislike c) like

3) Many houses in the past were constructed principally from wood.
   a) mainly b) often c) only

4) Larger birds sometimes have to run before they can get airborne.
   a) flying b) going c) in the air

5) Velcro is an incredibly practical type of fastener.
   a) useful b) new c) easy

Understanding 1

Look at the reading passage and choose the correct expression.

1) Leonardo da Vinci was ------- as the inventor of some modern flying machines.
   a) mistaken b) honoured c) credited

2) One of the principal ------- for the wings on Leonardo's flying machine came from a creature that usually flies at night.
   a) inspirations b) materials c) patterns

3) The ------- would pedal a crank while lying on a flat board.
   a) driver b) inventor c) pilot

4) Leonardo da Vinci's glider could be controlled by the pilot s________________ his weight.

5) The inventors of the first successful flying machine were able to ________________ Leonardo da Vinci's knowledge.

Understanding 2

Look at the reading passage again and decide if the following statements are true or false. Be ready to explain your choice.

1) T / F Leonardo da Vinci specialized in many different areas.

2) T / F Leonardo da Vinci often bought birds as pets.

3) T / F The pilot of Leonardo's flying machine could use both legs and arms to provide power.

4) T / F A very strong man could have made Leonardo da Vinci's ornithopter fly.

5) T / F Leonardo da Vinci's ideas for controlling a glider were mistaken.

Dictation

05

Listen and fill in the blanks using the words below:

recently	crowds	open	blank	appears
meantime	empty	entered	exactly	painting
gangs	picture	understand	discovered	appeared

Would you go to an art gallery to look at a 1. ______________ space on a wall? That is 2. ______________ what many did at the Louvre in Paris in 1911. They were going to look at the space where until 3. ______________ Leonardo da Vinci's 'Mona Lisa' had hung. On Monday, August 21st of that year, a man had 4. ______________ the famous gallery and calmly stolen the iconic 5. ______________. The Louvre was closed on Mondays, and so the theft was not 6. ______________ for 24 hours. A massive hunt began, and in the 7. ______________, images of the painting 8. ______________ all over the city. People were so intrigued that they came in 9. ______________ to look at the empty space where the 10. ______________ had been!

Think about it

Using the following information on Leonado's ornithopter, try to draw a diagram of how it might have looked.

Leonardo da Vinci's ornithopter was quite a large machine. The total length of the wings was around ten metres, and they were shaped like a bat's wings. The machine was made from pine wood and silk. There was a central wooden board on which the pilot would lie, face down. He would use his legs to pedal a crank. This crank was connected to a rod and pulley device that would provide the power for the flying machine. The ornithopter also had a hand crank, which would provide extra power. A mechanism that was operated by the pilot's head would enable the flying machine to be steered.

Go to page 98 for a further activity.

Unit 3 James Watt (1736-1819)

James Watt

Pre-Reading

Answer the following questions with a partner:

1) What changed during the Industrial Revolution?
2) The Industrial Revolution started in Britain. Can you think of any reasons why it might have started there?
3) How did people move heavy objects before the Industrial Revolution?
4) This unit will look at steam engines, but how are modern engines powered?
5) Is steam power still used today? Can you think of any examples?

Reading text

06

The Industrial Revolution, which lasted from around 1760 to 1820, transformed the world and was the beginning of the modern age. This significant change in the way people produced and transported goods began in Great Britain, and many of the innovations that shaped it were of British origin. By 1820, Britain had become the world's leading commercial nation.

Industry needs energy and power to drive the machines that make the mass production and easy movement of goods possible. Before the Industrial Revolution, most power was generated by water and wind. The harnessing of steam power, however, would change everything and make the revolution possible. When we think of steam power, one name that stands out is James Watt, who was born in Scotland in 1736.

There is a story that James Watt came up with the idea for the steam engine while watching a boiling kettle. He noticed that the steam from the boiling water was pushing the lid up, and he realized then the potential power of steam. Like many 'stories' from history, this is not exactly true. Watt did indeed study the way steam affected objects, but the steam engine had already been invented. What Watt did was to make it much more efficient, and therefore create the driving force for the Industrial Revolution.

James Watt had been working with the University of Glasgow, maintaining and repairing scientific instruments, when he began to experiment with steam engines. In 1764, he was asked to repair a Newcomen steam engine. This was the most advanced steam engine of the day and was used mainly for pumping water from mines. After repairing the engine, Watt realized that it was still not working very well.

He deduced that much of the thermal energy of the steam was being used in heating the engine cylinder on every cycle. This was wasted energy, as later in the cycle cold water was injected into the cylinder to condense the steam and reduce pressure. The heating and cooling process wasted thermal energy that could have been converted into mechanical energy. Watt concluded that a separate condenser needed to be added to the engine. This would free up more energy in the cylinder and make the engine much more efficient.

Coming up with an idea was one thing, but actually creating a working model of the new engine would take money and hard work. One of the challenges was producing precision iron components, as most ironworkers of the day were not so skilled. Watt eventually saw his steam engine produced in 1778. First used in mines, Watt's engine was modified and improved and came to be used in mills and factories, as well as powering boats and steam locomotives.

James Watt's impact on the Industrial Revolution cannot be underestimated. He went on to develop the concept of horsepower, and the unit of power, the 'watt', was named after him. He died at the age of 83, a wealthy and successful man.

MEMO

Vocabulary

The underlined word appears in the text. Choose the word below which best matches the underlined word.

1) The world of engineering has seen many significant innovations over the years.
   a) setbacks　b) changes　c) inventions

2) Solar panels can generate enough energy to power a house.
   a) create　b) upload　c) move

3) Modern cars are much more efficient than the cars of fifty years ago.
   a) effective　b) dangerous　c) interesting

4) The scientist came to his deduction after doing many experiments.
   a) laboratory　b) senses　c) conclusion

5) When designing a building, an architect must use precise measurements.
   a) accurate　b) simple　c) many

Understanding 1

Look at the reading passage and choose the correct expression.

1) The ------- of products was made possible by innovations in energy and power.
   a) marketing　b) sale　c) mass production

2) The Industrial Revolution led to Britain becoming the foremost ------- country in the world.
   a) commercial　b) production　c) agricultural

3) It was while at the University of Glasgow that Watt first ------- with steam engines.
   a) played　b) experimented　c) interacted

4) The temperature change in Newcomen's engine caused by adding cold water wasted t______________ energy.

5) Watt's solution to the wasted energy in Newcomen's engine was to add a separate ______________.

Understanding 2

Look at the reading passage again and decide if the following statements are true or false. Be ready to explain your choice.

1) T / F The ability to control and use steam power was fundamental to the success of the Industrial Revolution.

2) T / F After watching a boiling kettle, Watt came up with the idea of the steam engine.

3) T / F Newcomen's steam engine was already outdated when James Watt first repaired one.

4) T / F The water injected into Newcomen's engine made the engine less efficient.

5) T / F James Watt's steam engine was immediately used in many different areas.

Dictation

07

Listen and fill in the blanks using the words below:

circles	angle	engine	multiplied	horses
train	work	experiment	multiply	power
efficient	divided	jobs	measure	dividend

In the 1780's, James Watt needed to convince people to buy his new steam 1. ______________. Many people were reluctant to change from the 2. ______________ they were using to pull machinery at the time. Watt therefore set up an 3. ______________ to prove his engine was more 4. ______________ than using horses. He measured a horse walking in 5. ______________ to turn a grindstone in a mill. He then 6. ______________ the distance it walked by its roughly 180 pounds of pulling force, 7. ______________ the time it took and came up with a new 8. ______________–horsepower. He then demonstrated the 9. ______________ of one of his engines. It turned out that one of Watt's engines did the 10. ______________ of 35 horses.

Think about it

The Following is a basic description of how a steam engine works. Read the description and draw a diagram showing the parts of a steam engine:

In a steam engine, superheated steam forces a piston to move back and forth in a cylinder. The piston is attached to a crankshaft by a connecting rod. The crankshaft converts the back and forth motion of the piston into rotary motion to drive the flywheel. There is an inlet valve at each end of the cylinder. Steam from one of the inlet valves forces the piston to move to the other end of the cylinder. Steam from the other inlet valve then pushes the piston back to its original position.

Go to page 99 for a further activity.

Unit 4 George Stephenson (1781-1848)

George Stephenson

Pre-Reading

Answer the following questions with a partner:

1) How often do you use trains?
2) Describe the different kinds of trains you can see in Japan.
3) How are modern trains powered?
4) How long will the proposed Maglev train take to travel from Tokyo to Nagoya?
5) What are some of the advantages of rail travel?

Reading text

08

Railways are part of everyday life for many people. We use them to commute, to go on trips, and to haul freight. Train designers are always pushing the boundaries of speed, with the current L0 Series Maglev trains being developed in Japan, capable of reaching speeds of over 600km/h.

Back in 1825, the steam train, ‘*Locomotion No.1*’ became the first engine to pull passengers on a public railway. *Locomotion No.1's* top speed was 24km/h, and it ran on the Stockton and Darlington Railway in England. The designers of this innovative machine were the father and son team of George and Robert Stephenson.

George Stephenson was known as ‘The Father of Railways’. Although he did not invent the first steam locomotive, his train designs were to revolutionize rail travel. He was born in 1781 in northern England. Because he came from a poor family who could not afford to educate him, he was illiterate until the age of 18. Working in the coal mines of northern England and Scotland, he developed an interest in engineering and invention.

Steam locomotives first started to be used to haul coal in mines during the early 1800's. Stephenson became interested in locomotive design around this time and became determined to improve the early models. Having spent several years making locomotives to be used inside mines, he was asked in 1821 to design and construct the Stockton and Darlington Railway. This line would connect various mines to the River Tees, where coal could be transported to other places. It would also become the world's first public railway.

One of the problems that Stephenson had to overcome was what material to use for the tracks. Although cast iron rails had been used previously for tracks, Stephenson decided to use wrought iron for this new railway. Wrought iron is less brittle and more malleable than cast iron and, therefore, was less likely to crack under the weight of the locomotives. One of the other innovations on this line was the gauge, or width, of the tracks. Stephenson decided that the gauge would be 4 feet 8 ½ inches, or 1,435mm. This became, and still is, the standard gauge for railways all over the world.

If you ever travel on trains, you will probably notice that, unlike roads, the route they take is usually flat. This is because steam trains lost most of their power if they had to go up even the smallest gradient. George Stephenson discovered this through experimentation, and he used the knowledge when his company constructed the Liverpool and Manchester Railway, completed in 1830. This was where Stephenson's most famous locomotive, *Rocket*, first made an appearance. A competition was held to decide who would build the locomotives for the line. *Rocket* won the competition, at one point reaching a speed of 58km/h, a new record.

George Stephenson and his son, Robert, changed the way people travelled, setting many of the standards for railways that are still followed today.

MEMO

Vocabulary

The underlined word appears in the text. Choose the word below which best matches the underlined word.

1) In ancient times, people often used animals to haul heavy objects.
   a) load   b) secure   c) pull

2) People who are illiterate may struggle to find a job.
   a) unable to read and write   b) stupid   c) blind

3) The line between Tokyo and Nagoya will go through many mountains.
   a) path   b) train   c) track

4) Glass is a very brittle material.
   a) tough   b) breakable   c) shiny

5) Climbers often have to trek up steep gradients.
   a) slopes   b) buildings   c) plains

Understanding 1

Look at the reading passage and choose the correct expression.

1) George Stephenson first became fascinated in engineering while working in -------.
   a) coal mines   b) railways   c) schools

2) Steam trains first carried ------- in the early 19th century.
   a) mines   b) people   c) coal

3) The material most commonly used to construct railway lines was --------.
   a) wood   b) iron   c) rails

4) The common g______________ for railway tracks is similar in many countries.

5) Stephenson provided the trains for the Liverpool and Manchester railway after the *Rocket* won a ______________.

Understanding 2

Look at the reading passage again and decide if the following statements are true or false. Be ready to explain your choice.

1) T / F George Stephenson designed the first locomotive.

2) T / F The Stockton and Darlington Railway was Stephenson's first experience with locomotives.

3) T / F George Stephenson had to consider the type of material suitable for railway tracks.

4) T / F Wrought iron is likely to break under a heavy load.

5) T / F Trains quite often go up and down hills.

Dictation

09

Listen and fill in the blanks using the words below:

disaster	break	killed	meet	greet
parallel	moment	carriage	accident	time
still	guests	walked	ran	guest

The opening of the Liverpool and Manchester Railway in 1830 was a great 1. ______________ in transportation history. However, the day also saw a tragic 2. ______________. Around halfway into the journey, the train carrying the special 3. ______________, including the Prime Minister, stopped for a 4. ______________. William Huskisson, the Member of Parliament for Liverpool, 5. ______________ along the line to 6. ______________ the Prime Minister, who was in another 7. ______________. However, he did not see Stephenson's *Rocket*, which was travelling on the 8. ______________ line. As he was about to shake hands with the Prime Minister, who was 9. ______________ in his carriage, the *Rocket* hit Huskisson. He became the first person to be 10. ______________ by a passenger train.

Think about it

Here are the basic parts of a steam locomotive:

crankshaft	piston	boiler	drive wheel
steam reservoir	slide valve	cylinder	

Use the words above to complete the following stages in a steam engine:

1) Coal is heated in the ______________ and turns water into steam.
2) The steam expands and moves into the ______________.
3) Here the steam is controlled by the ______________.
4) Steam then moves into the ______________.
5) The pressure from the steam pushes the ______________, which is attached to a ______________.
6) This turns the ______________, which creates motion.

With this information on the essentials of a steam engine, draw and label a basic diagram of a steam locomotive.

Go to page 100 for a further activity.

Unit 5 Isambard Kingdom Brunel (1806-1859)

Isambard Kingdom Brunel

Pre-Reading

Answer the following questions with a partner:

1) What is the longest bridge you have ever crossed?
2) Have you ever travelled through a tunnel that goes under water? Where was it?
3) How long do you think it would take to sail from the U.K. to the U.S.?
4) Have you ever been on a sea journey? Where did you go?
5) Who is the most famous engineer you can think of?

Reading text

10

In the world of engineering, one name that should be well known to anyone interested in the topic is Isambard Kingdom Brunel. This Englishman was probably one of the most prolific mechanical and civil engineers who ever lived. Indeed, in a 2002 BBC poll to find 100 Great Britons, he finished 2nd, just behind Winston Churchill.

Brunel was responsible for the design and construction of tunnels, bridges, dockyards, long-distance railway lines and steamships at a time when Victorian Britain was the most powerful economic force in the world. Many of his designs were innovative, including the first tunnel under a navigable river, and the first iron ship to be driven by a screw propeller. Although he only lived to be 53 years old, Brunel's engineering output was immense, and much of what he built is still in use to this day.

Isambard Kingdom Brunel was born in Portsmouth, England, in 1806. His father was a French civil engineer, named Marc Isambard Brunel, and his mother was an English lady named Sophia Kingdom. This is where Brunel's unusual name came from. He was first taught technical drawing by his father and then continued his engineering studies in France, returning to England in 1822.

The Thames Tunnel, the Clifton Suspension Bridge and the Great Western Railway are three of Brunel's best known achievements. All three are still in use today. The Thames Tunnel, as mentioned earlier, the first under a navigable river, is today part of the London Overground, which, despite the name, has some sections that go underground. The Clifton Suspension Bridge, which stretches over the River Avon in western England, had the largest span of any bridge in the world at the time. It is still standing and is used by over 4 million vehicles every year. Running from London to Bristol, the Great Western Railway included Box Tunnel, at the time the longest railway tunnel in the world. Box tunnel, like much of the line, is still in use today.

It was transatlantic steamships, however, that consumed much of Brunel's later life. He was keen to extend his Great Western Railway transport network from Bristol to

New York. It was widely believed at the time that commercial steam voyages across the Atlantic would not be viable. People thought that the ships would have to carry so much fuel that there would not be enough space for any cargo. Brunel realized that the size of the ship was important. A larger ship would use proportionately less fuel for its size than a smaller ship carrying the same amount of cargo. This was due to the amount of resistance encountered in the water.

In 1838, *The Great Western* was completed. At 72 metres, it was the longest ship in the world at the time. The maiden voyage across the Atlantic was completed in 15 days and 5 hours, and the ship had coal to spare when it reached New York. For his next ship, the 98 metre *Great Britain*, Brunel pushed the boundaries of engineering even further. This vessel was the first transatlantic ship to be built mainly of iron rather than wood. It was also the first to use a propeller wheel as opposed to a paddle wheel.

Isambard Kingdom Brunel probably deserves to be remembered as one of the world's foremost engineers. His greatest legacy, however, is in the structures he designed and built, many of which are still in use today.

MEMO

Vocabulary

The underlined word appears in the text. Choose the word below which best matches the underlined word.

1) The writer was very prolific, writing three new books every year.
   a) clever b) slow c) productive

2) The hotel was immense, with over 1000 rooms.
   a) huge b) old c) amazing

3) The span of a large bird's wings can be up to three metres.
   a) weight b) height c) length

4) It was believed for a long time that space travel would not be viable.
   a) possible b) safe c) easy

5) The Wright brothers made their maiden flight in 1903.
   a) amazing b) first c) historic

Understanding 1

Look at the reading passage and choose the correct expression.

1) Building a passage under a ------- river was one of Brunel's many accomplishments.
   a) deep b) wide c) navigable

2) The Clifton Suspension Bridge was among one of Brunel's most famous -------.
   a) achievements b) positions c) characters

3) In the second part of his life, Brunel was ------- by a wish to see steamships cross the Atlantic.
   a) saddened b) interested c) consumed

4) Brunel understood that r________________ in the water was more important than the fuel consumed in large ships.

5) *The Great Britain* was the first ocean-going ________________ to be made of iron instead of wood.

Understanding 2

Look at the reading passage again and decide if the following statements are true or false. Be ready to explain your choice.

1) T / F Among other things, Brunel constructed areas in which to maintain and build ships.

2) T / F Brunel's unique name only came from his father.

3) T / F Train travellers in England can still experience going through Box Tunnel.

4) T / F Before Brunel, people thought that big ships would need to carry lots of fuel.

5) T / F *The Great Western* had used up all its fuel by the time it arrived in New York.

Dictation

11

Listen and fill in the blanks using the words below:

thought	construction	ascends	usually	southwest
shine	through	longest	sought	southeast
eastern	actually	descends	shines	usual

One of Isambard Kingdom Brunel's many achievements was the 1. ______________ of Box Tunnel. This was a railway tunnel on the Great Western Line in 2. ______________ England, which was completed in 1841. At the time, it was the 3. ______________ railway tunnel in the world at 2.95 kilometres. It also 4. ______________ on a 1 in 100 gradient from its 5. ______________ side. Every year, the sun 6. ______________ through the tunnel in April. It was 7. ______________ that Brunel deliberately aligned the tunnel for the sun to shine 8. ______________ on his birthday, April 9th. In fact, the sun 9. ______________ shines through the tunnel on the 6th of April, which is 10. ______________ the birthday of Brunel's sister.

Think about it

Using the following information, draw a diagram of Brunel's 'tunnelling shield'.

The Thames Tunnel was the world's first underwater tunnel. Although Isambard Kingdom Brunel spent some time working on the tunnel, the project was actually completed by his father, Marc Brunel.

These days, underwater tunnels are constructed using huge tunnel-boring machines, sometimes called 'moles'. However, this technology was not available in the 19th century.

Marc Brunel invented a 'tunnelling shield'—this was a big rectangular iron wall with lots of small shutters in it. Workers would open the shutters and dig out a layer of dirt. The shield would then be pushed forward a short distance. As the shield advanced, workers would shore up the tunnel behind it with a thick brick wall.

Go to page 100 for a further activity.

Unit 6 Nikolaus Otto (1832-1891)

Nikolaus Otto

Pre-Reading

Answer the following questions with a partner:

1) How many different car manufacturers can you name?
2) Can you drive a car or ride a motorbike?
3) What fuels are used to power modern-day engines?
4) In what way do you think engines will develop in the future?
5) Will the internal combustion engine continue to be used in the future?

Reading text

12

Nowadays, we take cars and motorcycles for granted, and many of us will expect to someday own at least one. The freedom that vehicles such as cars and motorbikes give us is thanks mainly to the invention that powers these machines—the internal combustion engine. It was the German, Nikolaus Otto, who first created a practical and usable internal combustion engine, and later the four-stroke engine. This four-stroke engine was the precursor to every combustion engine that has been built since.

Nikolaus Otto was born in the village of Holzhausen, Germany in 1832. He was from a modest background, and although doing well at school, he left aged 16, without completing his studies. Otto became a salesman, and it was while working in Frankfurt, where he sold tea, coffee and sugar, that he became interested in new technologies.

In 1860, Otto heard about a new gas-powered engine, which had been invented by a Belgian, Étienne Lenoir. This was the first workable and commercial internal combustion engine. Up to this point, engines had been powered by energy created by external combustion, as in a steam engine. Lenoir's engine, however, was noisy, inefficient and expensive. Otto, along with his brother, believed that they could build a liquid-fuelled engine, which they thought would work better.

The brothers encountered some setbacks as they tried to develop their engine, mainly to do with getting a patent for their design. His brother having dropped out of the project, Otto continued on his own. He eventually teamed up with Eugen Langen, a technician and sugar factory owner, who saw potential in Otto's design. The pair completed their first production engine, a two-stroke, which improved on the Lenoir design by compressing the gas before it was ignited. In 1867, Otto and Langen won the Gold Medal at the Paris World Exhibition for their gas engine.

Otto realized that his engine could still be improved, and his breakthrough came with the development of the four-stroke engine, or 'Otto Cycle Engine', in 1876. The 'four strokes' were as follows: 1) a downward *intake* stroke of the piston draws air and gas into the cylinder. 2) The mixture is compressed on the upward *compression* stroke of the piston. 3) The mixture is ignited by a spark plug, driving the piston downward again in the *combustion* (sometimes called the *power*) stroke. 4) The second upward *exhaust* stroke of the piston pushes the exhaust gas out of the cylinder.

Although there were various other inventors who claimed to have come up with the four-stroke idea before Otto, it was the Otto Cycle that came to be used in future car engines. Otto himself did not see the engine as being used in vehicles, but rather for stationary machines, such as might be found in mines and factories. This led to a split with one of his business partners, Gottlieb Daimler, who saw the engine being used for automobiles. The Daimler and Benz automobile companies, each of which produced the first liquid petroleum engine cars and later merged, used Otto's designs to create the engines that we use in automobiles today.

MEMO

Vocabulary

The underlined word appears in the text. Choose the word below which best matches the underlined word.

1) A usable machine is ready to use without needing any changes.
   a) working   b) broken   c) perfect

2) Many successful people come from quite modest backgrounds.
   a) rich   b) special   c) humble

3) If machinery is inefficient, it may need to be altered.
   a) unproductive   b) efficient   c) complicated

4) Recent breakthroughs in driverless cars could change how we move around.
   a) setbacks   b) developments   c) studies

5) The guard outside the castle was stationary.
   a) sleeping   b) unmoving   c) standing

Understanding 1

Look at the reading passage and choose the correct expression.

1) Otto's four-stroke engine became the model for future engines; it was the ------- to the modern engine.
   a) trademark   b) precursor   c) successor

2) Before Otto's contribution, Étienne Lenoir had already invented a ------- engine.
   a) workable   b) new   c) successful

3) The factory owner, Eugen Langen, realized that Otto's engine had --------.
   a) character   b) setbacks   c) potential

4) A spark plug causes a small explosion in the air and gas mixture of an engine, d______________ the piston down.

5) Because of a disagreement as to how the four-stroke engine should be used, Otto and his business partner Daimler ______________.

Understanding 2

Look at the reading passage again and decide if the following statements are true or false. Be ready to explain your choice.

1) T / F Cars and motorbikes are everyday things for most of us.

2) T / F Nikolaus Otto began working with engines as soon as he left school.

3) T / F One benefit of Lenoir's gas-powered engine was that it was quiet.

4) T / F The energy created by a four-stroke engine comes during the third stroke.

5) T / F Otto's four-stroke concept was only ever used for factory machines.

Dictation

13

Listen and fill in the blanks using the words below:

star	plan	air	merged	ambition
pair	therefore	become	merge	represent
surrounded	products	combine	became	ambitious

You may be familiar with the iconic emblem of the Mercedes Benz car company. The three-pointed star has come to 1. ______________ quality and reliability in automobile 2. ______________. But what does the emblem actually mean? When the Daimler and Benz car companies 3. ______________ in 1926, they decided to 4. ______________ their logos. Daimler was using the three-pointed 5. ______________ logo, and Benz was using a laurel wreath logo. The new emblem was a three-pointed star 6. ______________ by a laurel wreath. Eventually, the company became Mercedes Benz, and the logo 7. ______________ just the star. It represents the company's 8. ______________ to dominate land, sea and 9. ______________ with its engines. The three points, 10. ______________, represent land, sea and air.

Think about it

Using the information provided in the text and given below, draw a labeled diagram showing the four stages of the Otto Cycle Engine.

The 'four strokes' were as follows: 1) a downward intake stroke of the piston draws air and gas into the cylinder. 2) The mixture is compressed on the upward compression stroke of the piston. 3) The mixture is ignited by a spark plug, driving the piston downward again in the *combustion* (sometimes called the *power*) stroke. 4) The second upward exhaust stroke of the piston pushes the exhaust gas out of the cylinder.

Go to page 101 for a further activity.

Unit 7 Gustave Eiffel (1832-1923)

Gustave Eiffel

Pre-Reading

Answer the following questions with a partner:

1) Which building do you think symbolizes Japan?
2) What is the tallest structure in Japan?
3) What do you think are the biggest challenges of building a tall structure?
4) Please think of three countries and name the building that is most famous in these countries.
5) Have you ever been to Paris? Would you like to go?

Reading text

14

Sometimes a building can come to symbolize a country: the Pyramids in Egypt, the Kremlin in Russia and the Taj Mahal in India. Arguably, one of the world's most famous constructions, and one that is inescapably linked to the city and country it stands in, is the Eiffel Tower. It is the most visited paid monument in the world, having welcomed over 200 million people since it was built in 1889. Standing at 324 metres tall at its highest point, it is the tallest structure in Paris. When it was constructed, it was the tallest man-made structure in the world.

The Eiffel Tower was named after the man who constructed it, Gustave Eiffel, sometimes referred to as 'The Magician of Iron'. This civil engineer was born in the French city of Dijon to a well-to-do family in 1832. The young Eiffel developed an interest in science partly due to the influence of an uncle, who owned a chemical works in Dijon. This led him to enroll in the famous higher education and research institute, École Centrale Paris, which specializes in engineering and science. Eiffel graduated near the top of his class in 1855 with a degree in chemistry.

After graduation, Eiffel found himself working in the railway industry. He became involved with bridge design, and in particular, bridges made of iron. His first big solo project was the construction of the Bordeaux Bridge in south-west France. Spanning a large river, this bridge would be 500 metres long, and Eiffel was only 27 years old when he completed it. He would go on to have a highly successful career in the railway industry, building bridges, locomotives and stations. However, it is for the iconic tower in Paris that he is best remembered.

To celebrate the centennial of the French Revolution, the 1889 World's Fair was to be held in Paris. A tower, initially designed by two employees in Eiffel's company, Emile Nouguir and Maurice Koechlin, was selected to be the exposition's centrepiece. The proposed structure would be over 300 metres tall, making it the largest man-made structure in the world at that time, and was therefore a massive engineering undertaking.

The levels of detail and precision involved in putting together the Eiffel Tower were simply staggering. In total 1,700 general drawings were made, and a further 3,629 detailed drawings of the 18,038 different parts were produced. All these drawings needed to be incredibly precise, often to the nearest 0.1mm. The various sections of the tower were constructed at a nearby factory and then transported to the site to be joined together with over 2.5 million rivets.

The tower was completed in two years, in time for the opening of the World's Fair, and was an immediate success with the public. On the various levels, visitors could buy a souvenir newspaper, actually printed in the tower, eat cake at a patisserie, or send a postcard from the post office at the top. At night, the tower was illuminated by hundreds of gas lamps.

Over 100 years later, Eiffel's wonder of engineering is still standing and still delighting visitors from across the globe.

MEMO

Vocabulary

The underlined word appears in the text. Choose the word below which best matches the underlined word.

1) Mt Fuji is inescapably associated with Japan.
   a) never b) unavoidably c) increasingly

2) Being well-to-do does not always bring happiness.
   a) born b) famous c) wealthy

3) Solo travel can often be lonely.
   a) occasional b) independent c) interdependent

4) The undertaking was massive and involved thousands of workers.
   a) project b) engineering c) building

5) When large cities are illuminated at night, they can be seen from space.
   a) lit up b) bright c) decorated

Understanding 1

Look at the reading passage and choose the correct expression.

1) The Eiffel Tower is one of the most well known ------- on Earth.
   a) constructions b) places c) things

2) Gustave Eiffel went to study at the École Centrale Paris after being ------- by a relative.
   a) persuaded b) influenced c) forced

3) The Eiffel Tower was not ------- designed by Gustave Eiffel, but by two workers at his company.
   a) in fact b) initially c) properly

4) The Eiffel Tower was chosen to be the c________________ of the 1889 World's Fair.

5) The different parts of the Eiffel Tower were not built on location, but ________________ to the site from elsewhere.

Understanding 2

Look at the reading passage again and decide if the following statements are true or false. Be ready to explain your choice.

1) T / F The Eiffel Tower is the tallest building in the world.

2) T / F Gustave Eiffel was not a successful student.

3) T / F The Eiffel Tower was not Gustave Eiffel's first engineering project.

4) T / F Exact measurements were very important for the tower's design.

5) T / F At first people were not that interested in the Eiffel Tower.

Dictation

15

Listen and fill in the blanks using the words below:

torch	welcome	arrived	landmark	idea
enters	gift	entrance	numbers	numerals
porch	goddess	dates	welcomed	date

The Eiffel Tower was not the only famous 1. ______________ built by Gustave Eiffel. He was also responsible for the construction of the Statue of Liberty. Standing at the 2. ______________ to New York harbour, this huge statue was a 3. ______________ from the people of France to the people of the United States in 1886. It represents Libertas, a Roman liberty 4. ______________. Liberty is another word for freedom. There is a 5. ______________ in the statue's right hand and a tablet in its left hand. The tablet has the Roman 6. ______________ July IV MDCCLXXVI (July 4th, 1776) inscribed on it. This, of course, is the 7. ______________ of the U.S. Declaration of Independence. The statue now represents the 8. ______________ of freedom, and has 9. ______________ people from all over the world as they have 10. ______________ in the United States.

Think about it

The following is a description of the Eiffel Tower. Read the description and then draw and label a diagram of the tower:

The Eiffel Tower is pyramidal in shape with slightly curved sides. It is 324 metres high and is divided into four parts, each of which is separated by a floor. Up to the second floor, the tower is constructed of four main pillars. From the second floor, the four pillars join to form one single pylon, which then rises vertically to the top. The floors are successively at altitudes of 57m, 115m and 276m. There is also an intermediate platform between the second and top floors at 196m, but it is not used nowadays.

Go to page 102 for a further activity.

Unit 8 Thomas Edison (1847-1931)

Thomas Edison

Pre-Reading

Answer the following questions with a partner:

1) How do you think people saw in the dark before the invention of the light bulb?
2) What invention do you think has had the biggest impact on home life?
3) Do you think that we rely on artificial light too much?
4) Are the people who are famous for certain inventions always the people who actually invented the item?
5) What do you know about Thomas Edison?

Reading text

16

Human beings tend to be uncomfortable in the dark. We feel more scared, and we are more likely to trip and fall over unseen objects. Since the beginning of human history, we have tried to create ways of seeing in the dark. Most of these have been dangerous, inefficient, or expensive. It wasn't until around 150 years ago that the means to create safe, efficient and cheap lighting was created. The man largely responsible for this was known as 'The Wizard of Menlo Park' and was one of the most prolific inventors in history.

Thomas Edison was born in Milan, Ohio in 1847, but when he was still a boy, his family moved to Port Huron, Michigan. It was here that he first earned money, selling candy and newspapers on the train. Like so many of our famous engineers and inventors, his journey to discovery started on the railroads. After his education was over, some of which had been at school and some at home, Edison began work as a telegraph operator for a rail company.

Partly due to his poor hearing, possibly because of a childhood accident, Edison began to experiment with finding a way to play back recorded telegraph messages. This led to his invention of the phonograph, a machine that played sounds recorded onto indentations on paper wrapped around a cylinder. This invention came in 1877, a year after he had given up his job and started his own research laboratory in Menlo Park, New Jersey. This research facility was the first of its kind in the world and would become the headquarters for Edison's creative endeavors.

It is for the invention of the light bulb, however, that Edison is best remembered. In fact, Thomas Edison did not actually invent the light bulb. What he did was to create a practical, cheap, safe and efficient light bulb, which would help to transform the lives of millions of people.

Edison wanted to create an efficient incandescent light bulb, in other words, a lamp that emits light as a result of being heated. The idea was for electricity to heat a thin strip of material, called a filament, until it becomes hot enough to glow. The filament would be located inside a glass vacuum bulb. The light produced had to be just the right brightness to light up a room. Previous light bulbs had been too bright for household use. The material used as a filament was therefore important. At first, Edison used platinum, but this was expensive. After experimenting with more than 6000 different materials, he eventually discovered that carbonized bamboo worked very well.

Edison once said that:

"Genius is one percent inspiration, ninety-nine percent perspiration."

The story of his struggle to find a suitable filament demonstrates this very well.

Thomas Edison became extremely famous and quite rich in his lifetime. He was particularly skillful at marketing both himself and his inventions. That he was a prolific and ingenious inventor is of no doubt. By the time of his death, he held 1093 U.S. patents, a record that stood until 2003.

MEMO

Vocabulary

The underlined word appears in the text. Choose the word below which best matches the underlined word.

1) There are many means of communicating.
   a) instruments b) situations c) ways

2) Old metal will often have many small indentations on its surface.
   a) pieces b) holes c) marks

3) The sports facility at the university is very modern.
   a) centre b) place c) equipment

4) Old food sometimes emits a bad smell.
   a) gives off b) turns c) uncovers

5) On dark nights, the lights glow brightly.
   a) reflect b) shine c) seem

Understanding 1

Look at the reading passage and choose the correct expression.

1) Part of Edison's job for the railroad company was receiving ------- messages.
   a) secret b) telegraph c) telephone

2) A desire to ------- messages led to Edison's invention of the phonograph.
   a) play back b) listen to c) translate

3) Edison was able to ------- the lives of many people by creating an efficient light bulb.
   a) transform b) understand c) entertain

4) In his search for the right f________________, Edison tried out many different materials.

5) As well as inventing many things, Edison was also very good at ________________ himself.

Understanding 2

Look at the reading passage again and decide if the following statements are true or false. Be ready to explain your choice.

1) T / F Humans have always had easy ways of seeing in the dark.

2) T / F Edison may have been inspired to find a way to play back telegraph messages because he had difficulty reading them.

3) T / F There had been many usable light bulbs before Edison created his version.

4) T / F Edison wanted to find a filament that did not glow too brightly.

5) T / F According to Edison, even a genius needs to work hard to create new inventions.

Dictation

17

Listen and fill in the blanks using the words below:

amazing	lost	lifespan	believe	makers
1914	last	burning	1940	deliberately
certainly	maker	certain	belief	dropped

It can be annoying if a light bulb suddenly blows, and you have to go out and buy a new one. 1. ________________ it or not, however, there is a light bulb that has been 2. ________________ since 1901. This is the Centennial Light in Livermore, California. It is said that this 3. ________________ light bulb is proof of planned obsolescence. This is the idea that manufacturers 4. ________________ make products that will stop working after a 5. ________________ amount of time. This concept probably began when light bulb 6. ________________ realized that if they made a product that would 7. ________________ for a very long time, they would not make so much money. In fact, the 8. ________________ of a light bulb in 1924 was 2,500 hours. By 9. ________________, it had 10. ________________ to 1,000 hours. It is believed that planned obsolescence is still used in many of the products we use to this day.

Think about it

As mentioned in the reading, Thomas Edison did not actually invent the light bulb. However, he did produce a practical, long-lasting device. Modern light bulbs have not changed much since Edison's time. Here is a description of a modern light bulb:

The base of the light bulb has a metal contact, with a screw thread contact just above it. These connect to an electrical circuit. The metal contacts are attached to two stiff wires, which are in turn connected to a metal filament made from tungsten. The filament sits in the middle of a glass bulb and is held up by a glass mount. The glass bulb is filled with an inert gas, such as argon. This creates a vacuum, which prevents the filament from catching fire.

Using the information above, draw and label a diagram of a light bulb.

Go to page 102 for a further activity.

Unit 9 Nikola Tesla (1856-1943)

Nikola Tesla

Pre-Reading

Answer the following questions with a partner:

1) While you have probably heard of Thomas Edison, have you ever heard of Nikola Tesla?
2) Do you know the difference between AC and DC power?
3) In how many different situations do we use electricity in our daily lives?
4) Do you know what kind of power your phone charger uses?
5) As a foreigner in the U.S., Nikola Tesla faced some difficulties. Do you think it is difficult for a foreigner to be accepted in a foreign country?

Reading text

18

If you had to name one person who was the inspiration for many of the devices we use today, it would be Nikola Tesla. Although not credited with their inventions, he was responsible for the conception of radar, x-rays, remote control and wireless communication. What he is credited with is the designing of the alternating current (AC) electrical system, a system still used to power our homes and businesses.

Born in Smiljan, a small town in what is now Croatia, but in 1856 was part of the Austrian empire, Nikola Tesla was one of five children. Regarded by some people as being a genius, his talent may have come from his mother, who although uneducated, invented small household appliances in her spare time. He went to the University of Prague and after graduating worked for some time at the Central Telephone Exchange in Budapest. It was while working here that Tesla came up with the idea for an induction motor, a motor that uses rotating magnetic fields.

Finding it difficult to progress with his motor, Tesla decided to move to the United States. He was 28 years old. With a letter of introduction, he found himself working for the famous inventor, Thomas Edison. At first, Tesla was welcomed into Edison's company and was seen as a hard and dedicated worker. He focused on trying to improve a street lighting system that Edison was working on. The two men fell out over an unpaid bonus however, and Tesla left the company after six months.

This was the beginning of a famous rivalry between these two pioneers of electrical power. Tesla was convinced that the alternating current (AC) electrical system using rotating magnetic fields was superior. Edison, on the other hand, favoured the direct current (DC) system. The AC system produces an electrical current that periodically reverses direction. DC current flows in only one direction. The major advantage of the AC system was that it could flow for many miles without the need for a power station. The DC system, on the other hand, would need a power station for every square mile.

Tesla received financial backing for his AC project and in 1895 designed the first AC hydroelectric power plant in the U.S. In 1896, the plant successfully powered the city of Buffalo.

Edison waged a propaganda campaign against Tesla and AC power, trying to convince people that it was dangerous, and that DC was preferable. He even electrocuted an elephant to death using AC power to try and prove his point!

In the end, it was AC power that came to be used to power the world. It was much more efficient and meant far fewer power stations. DC power is still used for smaller items, such as battery chargers, but it is AC power that generates mains electricity for much of the world.

Nikola Tesla never got the recognition for his achievements in his lifetime. This was partly because Edison was such a powerful figure, and also partly because Tesla was a foreigner. He died almost penniless in 1943. Recently though, his name is back in the public eye, with the Tesla motor company, named after Nikola Tesla. Funded by Elon Musk, a famous entrepreneur, this car manufacturer has succeeded in making the first commercial fully electric-powered car. The name Tesla deserves to be remembered as someone who helped to power the modern world.

MEMO

Vocabulary

The underlined word appears in the text. Choose the word below which best matches the underlined word.

1) Some people believe that Leonardo da Vinci was responsible for the conception of the helicopter.
   a) creation b) building c) construction

2) Electric fans usually have four rotating arms.
   a) alternating b) long c) spinning

3) She was so dedicated that she practiced every day.
   a) enthusiastic b) good c) tired

4) James periodically changed the furniture round in his room.
   a) always b) sometimes c) frequently

5) The two countries waged a trade war against each other.
   a) ended b) settled c) conducted

Understanding 1

Look at the reading passage and choose the correct expression.

1) Tesla's mother liked to make useful ------- for her home.
   a) inventions b) appliances c) devices

2) Tesla and Edison had a ------- because of a financial issue.
   a) system b) company c) rivalry

3) Tesla preferred the AC system. Edison, on the other hand, ------- DC.
   a) favoured b) invented c) distrusted

4) Buffalo got its electricity from a p______________ that used AC power.

5) Although Nikola Tesla is famous now, he never received ______________ when he was alive.

Understanding 2

Look at the reading passage again and decide if the following statements are true or false. Be ready to explain your choice.

1) T / F Nikola Tesla invented the x-ray.

2) T / F Tesla was still quite young when he first thought up the induction motor.

3) T / F AC systems require power stations every three to four miles.

4) T / F Thomas Edison was prepared to kill animals to prove that his system was better than Tesla's.

5) T / F Like Edison, Tesla died a wealthy man.

Dictation

19

Listen and fill in the blanks using the words below:

serve	shopping	habits	between	later
behind	alone	page	ahead	stimulate
serves	stopping	age	habit	exercise

As well as being a very gifted inventor, Nikola Tesla also had some peculiar 1. ______________. After work each day he would dine, usually 2. ______________, at one particular restaurant, Delmonico's. 3. ______________, he changed to the Waldorf-Astoria Hotel. He always telephoned 4. ______________ with his order to the headwaiter, and it was always the same man who would 5. ______________ him. After dinner, Tesla returned to work, often not 6. ______________ until two or three in the morning. In 7. ______________ working, he would walk from eight to ten miles every day for 8. ______________. He also believed that if he curled his toes one hundred times for each foot every night, it would 9. ______________ his brain cells. These routines seemed to work, as Tesla lived until the ripe old 10. ______________ of 86 years old.

Think about it

As mentioned in the reading, Tesla and Edison were involved in a disagreement over which electrical system would be better to power American life. This became known as 'The War of the Currents'. In the end, Tesla's system became the one commonly used to power homes and businesses.

Using the following description of these two systems given in the passage:

> The AC system produces an electrical current that periodically reverses direction. DC current flows in only one direction.

Draw two labeled diagrams showing how these two systems work.

Go to page 103 for a further activity.

Unit 10 Henry Ford (1863-1947)

Henry Ford

Pre-Reading

Answer the following questions with a partner:

1) What is the most popular car manufacturer in your country?
2) What are the advantages of being able to mass-produce a product?
3) How could having a car change a person's life?
4) Do you think that cars are too expensive?
5) If you could choose any kind of car to own, what would you have?

Reading text

20

If you drive a car today, in some part you owe a debt of gratitude to Henry Ford. Before he made cars affordable for ordinary Americans by revolutionizing the means of automobile production, it was only the very rich who could enjoy driving.

Henry Ford's journey began in Dearborn, Michigan, in 1863. He was born on a farm and at a young age had a talent for taking clocks and watches apart and putting them back together again. He was not so interested in farm life, and at the age of 16, he headed for Detroit. Here, he worked as a machinist for a shipbuilding firm before going on to take a job servicing steam engines.

In 1891, Ford took up a position as an engineer for the Edison Illuminating Company. It was here that he developed an interest in the horseless carriage. These were the precursors to the modern car. Ford built various models before eventually meeting Thomas Edison himself, who persuaded him to keep on trying to develop a better automobile. By 1899, Ford had decided to leave the Edison Company and start out on his own, designing motorcars. He worked with various backers and investors until he was able to found the Ford Motor Company in 1905.

Henry Ford believed that cars should be available to the average working American. He wanted a car that could be driven on the rough track roads that crisscrossed the American countryside. He also wanted a car that was durable and easy to repair. His solution was a vehicle that was to open the world of driving to the common man—the Model T.

Cars had already been around for decades, but they were expensive to build and could only really be owned by wealthy people. When Henry Ford unveiled his Model T in 1908, it cost $850, the equivalent of $22,500 in today's money. By 1925, the price had dropped to $260, $3,625 in today's money. This availability of personal transport was to have a massive impact on society and would change the way people lived their lives.

How was the Ford Motor Company able to produce cars for such a low price? The answer was simple and ingenious. The moving assembly line was already being used in slaughterhouses, where a Ford Company employee, William Klann, observed how efficient the work was. One worker basically stayed in position and performed the same task repeatedly. The idea was taken up at Ford, and soon the Model T production time had gone down from 12.5 hours in 1910 to under 2 hours by 1914. This meant that the price of the car could be lowered.

By 1918, more than half of the cars on American roads were Model T's. Henry Ford himself became a wealthy and influential man. He was good to his staff, and in 1914 he doubled the pay of his workers to $5 a day. He also reduced the working week to 40 hours, with five 8-hour days a week.

MEMO

Vocabulary

The underlined word appears in the text. Choose the word below which best matches the underlined word.

1) Engineers and inventors have made our lives much easier, and we owe them our gratitude.
   a) thanks b) lives c) money

2) Servicing complex machines is very important.
   a) making b) creating c) maintaining

3) The new plan had many backers.
   a) supporters b) members c) enemies

4) Machine parts need to be durable.
   a) strong b) long-lasting c) expensive

5) Complicated problems sometimes need ingenious answers.
   a) imaginative b) difficult c) easy

Understanding 1

Look at the reading passage and choose the correct expression.

1) Ford's new methods of making cars meant that they were ------- for many people.
   a) possible b) affordable c) new

2) After trying various car designs, Ford was ------- by Thomas Edison not to give up.
   a) employed b) ordered c) persuaded

3) The U.S. was ------- by many uneven trails.
   a) crisscrossed b) driven c) opened

4) Ford's cheap cars meant that many people had their own transport, which had a m______________ impact on their lives.

5) The assembly line was modeled on those already being used in ______________.

Understanding 2

Look at the reading passage again and decide if the following statements are true or false. Be ready to explain your choice.

1) T / F Henry Ford was good at designing cars, but no good at fixing clocks and watches.

2) T / F Some people gave Ford money to help him start his company.

3) T / F The Model T was one of the very first cars ever made.

4) T / F On an assembly line, many people do a variety of different tasks.

5) T / F Ford treated his workers very well.

Dictation

21

Listen and fill in the blanks using the words below:

firm	prove	film	drive	returning
move	highest	leaving	drives	exactly
higher	dealer	returns	journey	superior

Driving a car up a mountain may seem far-fetched, but that is 1. ______________ what Henry Alexander Jr. did in May, 1911. Henry Jr. was challenged by his father, who was also called Henry, to 2. ______________ a Model T Ford to the top of Ben Nevis. At 1,345m, Ben Nevis is the 3. ______________ mountain in Scotland. Henry Sr. was a motor 4. ______________ who was importing the new Model T from the United States. He believed that the car was 5. ______________ to British models and came up with the challenge to 6. ______________ his point. The ascent took 5 days, with the team 7. ______________ the car on the mountain and 8. ______________ to the town of Fort William to sleep each night. The 9. ______________ was made more difficult because there was still snow on the mountain. In 2015, 10. ______________ was found of the Model T descending the mountain.

Think about it

Henry Ford was the first automobile manufacturer to successfully use the assembly line to construct his Model T Ford.
Use the description below to draw a diagram of an assembly line:

An assembly line works on the principle of having each worker at a separate post, usually performing one particular operation. The parts of the product move from one worker to the next, usually on a conveyer belt. Heavier items will be moved by overhead cranes or by a forklift truck. The men and the tools they need will be in the sequence of the operation so that each component should travel the least possible distance between each worker.

Go to page 104 for a further activity.

Unit 11 Guglielmo Marconi (1874-1937)

Guglielmo Marconi

Pre-Reading

Answer the following questions with a partner:

1) Do you ever communicate with people in other countries?
2) What methods can be used to communicate with people in other countries?
3) How do you think people from other countries communicated with each other in the past?
4) Before intercontinental communication became normal, what kind of communication problems could occur?
5) In what ways do you think wireless communication could help to save lives?

Reading text

22

There are many things that we take for granted in modern life. One of these is that we can listen live to what people are saying thousands of miles away. Imagine that you are in trouble many miles from civilization. If you have a radio transmitter, you have a chance of being saved because of wireless technology. The man who first successfully sent wireless signals over a great distance was the Italian inventor and engineer, Guglielmo Marconi.

Marconi was born in Bologna, Italy, in 1874. He was the son of wealthy parents; his father was an Italian nobleman, and his mother was from the Irish Jameson whiskey family. The young Marconi spent some years living in England before returning to Italy. He was mostly schooled at home, and subsequently attended the Livorno Technical Institute and then the University of Bologna (the world's oldest university). It was while at Livorno that he developed an interest in wireless technology.

In 1888, the German physicist Heinrich Hertz first proved the existence of electromagnetic waves, or 'radio' waves. There was great interest in this discovery from the scientific community. Marconi was also fascinated by radio waves, and then started to experiment with them in the attic of his father's house. Unlike many others, he saw the potential for communication technology. He ended up managing to send signals up to a mile away. However, failing to get much interest in his work, he moved to England in 1896.

After arriving in England, Marconi soon found groups, including the British Post Office, interested in what he was doing with radio waves. He began to send signals further and further, and in 1897, sent the first-ever wireless communication over open sea. This was followed by signals sent across the English Channel to France. Transmitters were also set up in lighthouses. Here they could be used to signal the coastguard if any ships ran aground.

Marconi now set his sights on transmitting across the Atlantic Ocean. Many people believed that this would be impossible because of the curvature of the Earth. It was thought that radio waves could only travel in straight lines. Marconi believed that the waves would follow the curve of the planet. In fact, radio waves do travel in straight lines, but they bounce off the ionosphere, therefore approximating a curve.

After some failed attempts, Marconi managed to send a signal from Cornwall in England to Newfoundland in Canada, a distance of 2100 miles. On December 12th, 1901, a faint, three-dot signal (the letter 'S' in Morse code) was received at Signal Hill, Newfoundland. The antenna that received the signal was attached to a kite flying 500 feet above the ground. A year later, the first actual radio message was sent across the Atlantic. In 1903, President Theodore Roosevelt sent a greetings message to King Edward VII.

Marconi received the Nobel Prize for Physics in 1909 for his contribution to the development of wireless technology. His technology would also prove invaluable when three years later the Titanic sank in the North Atlantic Ocean. Marconi wireless operators stationed on the ship were able to send a distress signal. This enabled another ship to come and rescue some 700 survivors.

MEMO

Vocabulary

The underlined word appears in the text. Choose the word below which best matches the underlined word.

1) Not living near civilization can be difficult, especially when the weather is bad.
   a) countryside b) inhabited areas c) cities

2) John first worked for a company, and subsequently he started his own business.
   a) soon b) after that c) finally

3) A local community member was responsible for cleaning the hall.
   a) group b) private c) interested

4) After taking on too much cargo, the ship ran aground.
   a) sank b) hit the bottom of the sea c) crashed

5) The explorers travelling to the Antarctic carried many invaluable supplies.
   a) vital b) extra c) interesting

Understanding 1

Look at the reading passage and choose the correct expression.

1) Coming from the Jameson whiskey family, Marconi's mother was ------- and well connected.
   a) aristocratic b) scientific c) wealthy

2) Marconi's experimentation with radio waves began -------.
   a) in the attic b) at school c) in England

3) Sending wireless signals over ------- was one of Marconi's achievements after arriving in England.
   a) open sea b) land c) England

4) It was believed that the Earth's c ______________ would make sending radio waves across oceans very difficult.

5) The first radio signal sent by Marconi across the Atlantic was very ______________ and not very long.

Understanding 2

Look at the reading passage again and decide if the following statements are true or false. Be ready to explain your choice.

1) T / F Marconi was not the first person to be interested in radio waves.

2) T / F Marconi found it difficult to get people interested in his work when he arrived in England.

3) T / F Marconi was correct about radio waves following the curve of the planet.

4) T / F The first radio signal sent across the Atlantic was received on the ground on December 12th, 1901.

5) T / F Marconi was awarded the Nobel Prize because his technology helped the Titanic.

Dictation

23

Listen and fill in the blanks using the words below:

senior	operator	captain	famous	message
near	picked	nearby	hitting	fitting
operators	thinking	sinking	water	wetter

"Come quick. Engine room nearly full." This was the last 1. ______________ sent by the Titanic before the ship sank after 2. ______________ an iceberg. This distress call was sent by Jack Phillips; one of the two Marconi wireless 3. ______________ on the doomed ship. In April, 1912, wireless technology was still new, and only the most 4. ______________ ships had operators. As they realized that the ship was 5. ______________, the two Marconi men sent out messages to 6. ______________ ships asking them to help. Jack Phillips, the 7. ______________ operator, did not leave his station even after being told he could stand down by the 8. ______________. He died in the freezing 9. ______________, but his heroism helped to save many of the survivors, who were 10. ______________ up by the other ships.

Think about it

Here is my birth month in Morse code:

__/._/._./_._./....

First developed by Samual F.B. Morse, Morse code is a method of sending text messages by using clicks, lights or on-off tones. It was first used to send messages by telegraph.

The letters of the alphabet and the numbers 0-9 are represented by a series of dots and dashes, or short signals and long signals. The most common letters in English have the shortest code, so 'E' is one dot and 'I' is two dots.

Check Morse code online and find out what my birth month is and then write your own birth month and name in Morse code.

Go to page 104 for a further activity.

Unit 12 Alan Turing (1912-1954)

Alan Turing

Pre-Reading

Answer the following questions with a partner:

1) What different things do you use your computer for?
2) How have computers changed people's lives?
3) In what situations would people use secret codes?
4) Do you know of any secret codes? What is the code?
5) Do you know what numbers are used to give computers instructions?

Reading text

24

From cars to smartphones, laptops to rockets, we live in a world dominated by computers. Modern computer technology has involved the work and ideas of many talented people. One of them is Alan Turing, who is often called '*The father of computer science*'. This remarkable but sometimes troubled man was only 41 years old when he died, but his impact on the modern world was huge.

Alan Turing was born in London, England in 1912. From an early age, he showed signs of being a genius. He also showed early signs of being determined to achieve his goals. At the age of 13, he was due to start at boarding school. However, his first day coincided with the 1926 General Strike. Not wanting to miss school, the young Turing cycled the 97km to his school alone, staying overnight at an inn.

After school, Turing went to Cambridge University, where he studied mathematics. After graduating with a first-class honours degree, he became a research fellow at Cambridge. In 1936, he published a paper in which he proposed the idea of a *Universal Machine*, later called the *Turing Machine*. This was a machine that was capable of computing anything that is computable and was the blueprint of the modern computer.

After Cambridge, Turing went on to study for his PhD at Princeton in the U.S. As well as mathematics, he also became interested in cryptology, the study of codes. This knowledge of codes and how to solve them was to lead to the event that Turing is best remembered for, the breaking of the Enigma code.

With the outbreak of World War II, Turing found himself back in England and working for the British government as a code breaker. He was based at Bletchley Park, the nerve-centre for Britain's code-breaking efforts.

The Germans had developed a sophisticated cipher, or code machine, to encode messages sent to the army, navy and air force, called Enigma. Half mechanical, half electrical, Enigma used jumbled up letters of the alphabet to create potentially hundreds of millions of different possible codes.

Turing and his team constructed a machine called *Bombe*, which was able to drastically reduce the number of possible code combinations coming from Enigma. The rest of the code breaking was done manually. It is estimated that by successfully breaking the Enigma code, the war was shortened by about two years, and millions of lives were saved.

Turing continued to work on his *Turing Machine* after the war. He understood that a computer needed memory to store numbers and a processor to calculate them. He also realized that these parts only needed instructions given in numbers. The only numbers needed were 1 and 0, in other words, a binary system. Turing's genius was to figure out that anything could be turned into numbers.

Despite doing so much for the war effort, Alan Turing's life ended in disgrace and tragedy. Gay, in a time when homosexuality was illegal in Britain, he was convicted of 'gross indecency' for living with another man. Two years later, Turing committed suicide by cyanide poisoning. In 2013, the man who helped to bring the world the computer was given an official pardon by the British government.

MEMO

Vocabulary

The underlined word appears in the text. Choose the word below which best matches the underlined word.

1) You can often achieve what you want if you work hard.
   a) get b) take c) understand

2) He proposed the idea without first checking all the available information.
   a) made b) put forward c) had

3) After the outbreak of war, many people have to leave their homes.
   a) middle b) end c) start

4) After the earthquake, Naomi's possessions were jumbled up all over the floor.
   a) mixed up b) set up c) turned up

5) Some machines still have to be operated manually.
   a) remotely b) by hand c) mechanically

Understanding 1

Look at the reading passage and choose the correct expression.

1) Even though Turing's first day at school ------- with industrial action, he was determined to get there.
   a) opened b) connected c) coincided

2) The machine that Turing proposed at Cambridge was ------- of working out almost anything.
   a) thinking b) capable c) making

3) Enigma was a very ------- machine for sending secret messages.
   a) sophisticated b) complicated c) useful

4) The number of code combinations coming from Enigma was d______________ reduced by the *Bombe* machine.

5) Because Alan Turing lived with another man, he was ______________ of what was seen in the day as a crime and subsequently killed himself.

Understanding 2

Look at the reading passage again and decide if the following statements are true or false. Be ready to explain your choice.

1) T / F Turing did not show any signs of being talented until he was an older man.

2) T / F Turing's *Universal Machine* was a model for the modern computer.

3) T / F The Enigma machine did not have a large number of possible codes.

4) T / F With the *Bombe*, Turing and his team could find all the possible code combinations.

5) T / F The breaking of the Enigma code had a huge impact on the war.

Dictation

25

Listen and fill in the blanks using the words below:

finished	miles	lower	stress	mile
scientist	seriously	slower	athlete	continued
presented	meetings	athletic	continues	prevented

As well as being a code-breaker and pioneering computer 1. ______________, Alan Turing was also almost an Olympic 2. ______________. He loved distance running and started to do it 3. ______________ as a schoolboy. He would often run the 31 4. ______________ from his home in Ely to university at Cambridge. While working at Bletchley Park, he would sometimes run the 40 miles to London for 5. ______________. He competed in a qualifying marathon for the 1948 Olympics and 6. ______________ in 5th place. His time was 2 hours and 46 minutes, only 11 minutes 7. ______________ than the eventual Olympic champion. A leg injury 8. ______________ him trying for any more Olympics, although he 9. ______________ running. He said that it was the only way he could relieve the 10. ______________ from his job.

Think about it

The Enigma code used jumbled up letters of the alphabet and was very complicated. However, we can make more simple codes. One of these is a '*Substitution code*' where a letter of the alphabet is replaced by another letter. Can you break the following substitution code? What should the message say?

H KHJD SN QDZC

What is the code?

Can you make a new code? Try to create a new code based on letters or numbers, or both, and try it out on the rest of the class.

Go to page 105 for a further activity.

Unit 13 Stephanie Kwolek (1923-2014)

Stephanie Kwolek

Pre-Reading

Answer the following questions with a partner:

1) In what kind of situations would you need to wear protective clothing?
2) What are the strongest materials you can think of?
3) What do you think is the strongest naturally occurring material?
4) Why do some important people get driven around in bulletproof cars?
5) Do you know of any female engineers who have made a great contribution to human life?

Reading text

26

Ever since gunpowder was first used to fire bullets, people have tried to find some way to protect themselves from these deadly projectiles. The invention of Kevlar made that desire a reality. Nowadays, soldiers and police officers routinely wear bulletproof vests. Presidents and other heads of state will often be driven around in bulletproof cars made with Kevlar. This incredibly tough material is also used for aircraft parts, space vehicles, building materials, tires, all kinds of protective clothing, and in over two hundred other products. It is difficult to estimate the number of people's lives that have been saved by Kevlar, but it probably runs into the thousands.

The woman behind the discovery of this amazing material was American, Stephanie Kwolek. She was born to Polish immigrants in Pennsylvania in 1923. Her father was a keen naturalist, and although he died when Kwolek was quite young, he gave her a lifelong interest in science. Her interest in fabrics came from her mother.

Kwolek wanted to be a doctor when she was young. After graduating from university with a degree in chemistry, she began to look for work to help pay for medical school. This was in the mid-1940's, when many men had still not returned home from World War II. This meant that Kwolek was able to get a position working for the DuPont Company. DuPont was heavily involved in the research and development of synthetic fibres, that is, fibres that have been made by chemical synthesis. Indeed, DuPont had recently been responsible for the creation of nylon. Kwolek enjoyed her work with DuPont so much that she decided to abandon her dream of becoming a doctor and stick with the company.

In the early 1960's, the U.S. was facing a gasoline shortage, and Kwolek and her team were tasked with trying to create a lightweight but strong fibre to be used for tires. Kwolek experimented with polymers: large molecules that are made from binding smaller units together. These can be made into fabrics or plastics. One day, she came up with a polymer solution that was much thinner than usual. Further work on the substance revealed it to be a very strong, stiff, lightweight material. In fact, it was five times stronger than steel.

DuPont immediately saw the potential for this new material, and further research was conducted. In 1971, Kevlar was introduced. Kwolek was not involved in the development of Kevlar as a commercial product and did not receive any royalties for her discovery, as she signed over the patent to DuPont. She did, however, continue to work on strengthening the product she had discovered. Kwolek received many awards and distinctions for her work, and in 1995, she was added to the National Inventors Hall of Fame, only the fourth woman to join this list. Kwolek continued working for DuPont until her retirement, and afterwards was actively involved in teaching and research. She died, aged 90, in 2014.

MEMO

Vocabulary

The underlined word appears in the text. Choose the word below which best matches the underlined word.

1) People working with dangerous equipment routinely carry out safety inspections.
   a) regularly b) sometimes c) seldom

2) Amateur cooks often have to estimate how long to boil things for.
   a) analyse b) count c) guess

3) If life is difficult, some people will tell you, 'Don't abandon hope!'
   a) give up b) have c) losing

4) The new substance had a very strange smell.
   a) product b) material c) food

5) A successful songwriter will often get royalties when their song is played in public.
   a) rewards b) recognition c) payment

Understanding 1

Look at the reading passage and choose the correct expression.

1) A bulletproof vest is a way to defend yourself from ------- that could kill you.
   a) material b) projectiles c) people

2) Kevlar is an ------- strong substance that has many uses.
   a) amazing b) incredibly c) unusually

3) A ------- material is one that is manmade.
   a) synthetic b) tough c) chemical

4) If the U.S. had not been f________________ a fuel shortage, Kevlar may not have been invented.

5) DuPont realized that the material Kwolek had discovered could be very useful, so they ________________ more tests.

Understanding 2

Look at the reading passage again and decide if the following statements are true or false. Be ready to explain your choice.

1) T / F We know exactly how many people's lives have been saved by Kevlar.

2) T / F Kwolek was influenced by both of her parents.

3) T / F DuPont only focused their research on natural fibres.

4) T / F Polymers are created from joining smaller elements together.

5) T / F Kwolek became rich because of her discovery.

Dictation

27

Listen and fill in the blanks using the words below:

proved	occurred	equals	image	stop
developed	labour	previously	outcomes	equal
imagine	step	fighting	occurs	previous

The outbreak of World War II was to change the lives of many people. Most of us have a negative 1. ______________ of war and its effects; however, there can be positive 2. ______________. For example, new technology is often 3. ______________ more quickly than in peacetime. Another positive effect that 4. ______________ during WWII was the working opportunity given to women. Because so many men were either 5. ______________ overseas or had been killed in action, there was a 6. ______________ shortage in some countries. Governments asked women to 7. ______________ in and do these jobs, many of which had only 8. ______________ been done by men. As a result, women 9. ______________ that they could do many of these jobs just as well as men. This was to lead to the workplace becoming more 10. ______________ in the years following the war.

Think about it

Kevlar is a polymer. The word 'polymer' comes from two Greek words, 'poly' meaning 'many' and 'mer' meaning 'part'. Polymers are made from 'monomers' ('mono' means 'one'), which are single small molecules. Monomers join together in a chain to create a polymer.

Monomers always have a carbon-to-carbon double bond. Here are three molecules of ethene:

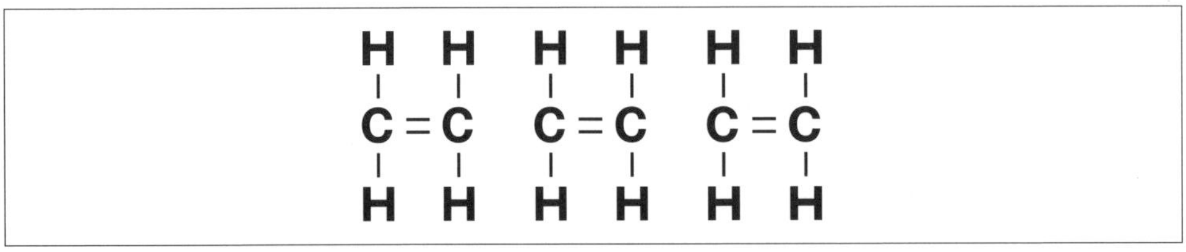

Joined together to make a polymer, they look like this:

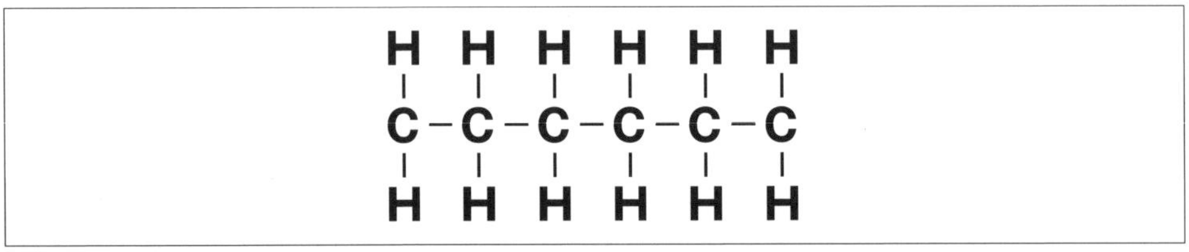

This is 'polyethene'. Notice that the carbon-to-carbon bonds are now single. Polymers can be very long, so scientists usually just draw a repeating unit. Using the instructions below, draw the repeating unit for polyethene:

Take two carbon atoms and draw them with all the hydrogen atoms joined to them. Next, extend the bonds from the two carbon atoms. Then, draw square brackets through the extended bonds. Finally, write a small 'n' next to the diagram to show that you have a large number of them.

Go to page 106 for a further activity.

Unit 14 Steve Wozniak (1950-)

Steve Wozniak

Pre-Reading

Answer the following questions with a partner:

1) Do you use Apple products? If yes, what kinds of products and why?
2) Have you ever queued to buy a new electronic product?
3) Personal devices are getting smaller and smaller. Do you think that they can be too small? Explain your answer.
4) Which do you find easier to use, Mac or Windows? Explain your answer.
5) Steve Jobs is more famous than Steve Wozniak. Why do you think this is?

Reading text

28

It is one of the most famous and valuable brands in the world. Every time it releases a new product, people spend days queuing up to be among the first to buy one. Its co-founder, Steve Jobs, famous for his demonstrations of the latest must-have gadget, became an icon of sleek, functional technology. However, the man who conceived and built the very first Apple computer was the other co-founder of this hugely successful company, Steve Wozniak.

Born in San Jose, California in 1950, Wozniak was probably partly influenced by his father, who worked in electronics. This love of electrical engineering grew as he went through school and university. Wozniak wanted a computer when he was a teenager, but at that time, computers were the size of rooms and very expensive. However, this did not stop him from designing computers on paper.

Wozniak's first working computer was built in 1971 with a friend, Bill Fernandez, and was called ‘Cream Soda’. This machine had no screen or keyboard, and programs were entered using punched cards. It was Fernandez who was to introduce Wozniak to Steve Jobs. At the time, Wozniak was working for the summer at Hewlett Packard designing calculators. Fernandez thought that Wozniak and Jobs would get on as they both shared an interest in electronics and liked playing pranks.

This turned out to be a fortunate meeting, and the world of computing was about to change forever. The pair began to work on a project to build a microcomputer with a video display. In 1975, a prototype of the first Apple computer was tested. This was the first time in history that a TV screen displayed characters produced by a home computer. In 1976, the Apple I was completed. Wozniak had designed the hardware, circuit boards and operating system for this breakthrough machine.

Wozniak and Jobs tried to sell their design to Hewlett Packard, but the company declined. This led to the two deciding to build and sell the computers themselves. They raised money by selling personal items and started to work in Jobs' parent's garage. The world's first buyer of Apple computers was the Byte Shop in Mountain View, California. On April 1st, 1976, Apple Computer was formed. The inspiration for the name came from a visit that Jobs made to a Californian apple orchard.

The Apple II followed soon after and was to be a major success. Wozniak had discovered a way to display colour graphics on the screen, having been inspired by an Atari computer game that he was coding. In 1980, Apple Computer went public and Wozniak and Jobs became rich.

One year later, Wozniak was injured in a small airplane crash and lost his memory. He was able to regain it, partly by playing computer games, but from this point he began to drift away from Apple. He felt that he was no longer able to focus on engineering and wasn't really interested in management. In 1985, he left the company.

We have Steve Wozniak to thank for floppy disks, external memory, colour on computer screens, and arguably the personal computer itself. He said, "*A personal computer should be small, reliable, convenient to use and inexpensive*". This reality has changed the lives of millions of people.

MEMO

Vocabulary

The underlined word appears in the text. Choose the word below which best matches the underlined word.

1) Functional machines are usually quite easy to use.
a) simple　　b) complicated　　c) practical

2) Many of the inventors who actually conceived the devices we use are not now famous.
a) created　　b) bought　　c) understood

3) A popular prank is to hide something from someone and pretend that you don't know where it is.
a) game　　b) practical joke　　c) sport

4) His proposal was good but was declined by the developers.
a) turned down　　b) accepted　　c) taken

5) A major disaster can cost a country a lot of money.
a) unexpected　　b) new　　c) big

Understanding 1

Look at the reading passage and choose the correct expression.

1) Some people are so keen to buy new Apple products that they sometimes can be found ------- up to buy one.
a) queuing　　b) looking　　c) turning

2) 'Cream Soda' was the first ------- machine made by Wozniak.
a) technical　　b) computer　　c) working

3) A ------- encounter between Wozniak and Jobs changed the world of computing forever.
a) fortunate　　b) business　　c) meeting

4) A visit to a fruit farm gave Steve Jobs the i______________ for the Apple name.

5) Wozniak was able to ______________ his memory by playing games.

Understanding 2

Look at the reading passage again and decide if the following statements are true or false. Be ready to explain your choice.

1) T / F It was Steve Jobs who actually built the first Apple computer.

2) T / F When Wozniak was young, buying your own computer was actually quite difficult.

3) T / F 1975 saw an important breakthrough in computer technology.

4) T / F Wozniak and Jobs were able to build their first computer after getting money from a big company.

5) T / F Steve Wozniak is still at the centre of the Apple Company.

Dictation

29

Listen and fill in the blanks using the words below:

pieces	passions	orders	beauty	force
exhibition	passion	jobs	stylish	forced
work	order	tiles	works	behind

The Apple co-founder Steve Jobs was always interested in the aesthetic 1. ________________ of objects. This is one of the reasons his Apple products always looked so 2. ________________. It was not just technology that interested him though. He also had a 3. ________________ for porcelain. He particularly liked the 4. ________________ of one Japanese artist based in Toyama. The artist's name is Yukio Shakunaga, and his style of porcelain is called 'Etchu Seto-yaki'. Jobs first saw Shakunaga's work at an 5. ________________ in Kyoto, where he bought several 6. ________________. After that, he kept in touch with the artist and bought more 7. ________________ over the years. The man 8. ________________ so much innovative computer technology was even 9. ________________ to buy a fax machine, as this was the only way he could place his 10. ________________ with Mr. Shakunaga!

Think about it

All of the information that is processed on a computer is in the form of a sequence of 1's and 0's. This number system, which only uses two digits, is called 'binary'.
As well as being used to encode data, binary can be used in other ways. A binary clock, for example, is an alternative to a traditional analogue clock or a digital clock.

Study the principle of a binary clock.

The first two columns of lights represent the hours.
The second two columns of lights represent the minutes.
The third two columns of light represent the seconds.
In each pair, the first column represents the ten's place and the second column represents the one's place.
The bottom row has a value of 1.
The second row has a value of 2.
The third row has a value of 4.
The top row has a value of 8.

Now, look at the following binary clock and work out what time it is in hours, minutes, and seconds.

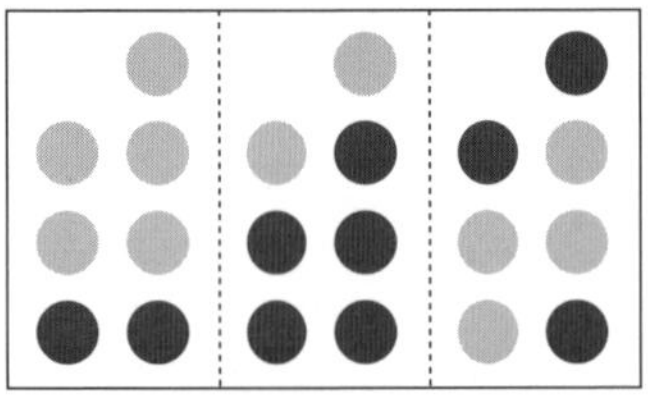

Try to make some new times using the binary clock system and ask your partner to work out the times.

Go to page 106 for a further activity.

Unit 15 Tim Berners-Lee (1955-)

Tim Berners-Lee

Pre-Reading

Answer the following questions with a partner:

1) Do you use the Internet regularly?
2) What do you usually use the Internet for?
3) What is the difference between the Internet and the World Wide Web?
4) What kind of webpages do you usually visit?
5) What might be some of the merits and demerits of the Internet?

Reading text

30

There is every chance that if you live in a fairly developed society, you will at some point visit a webpage. You may be checking some information, watching a music video, consulting a recipe or just catching up on the day's news. For many of us, the World Wide Web, often just referred to as 'The Web', is a daily part of our lives. In fact, it has transformed the lives of many people and changed the way we communicate and gather information. You might think that something so big and life changing was the work of a large group of scientists. Actually, the credit for the invention of the World Wide Web goes to one man: Tim Berners-Lee.

Berners-Lee was born in London, England in 1955. His parents were computer scientists, and the young Berners-Lee often liked to play with model railways, which gave him an interest in electronics. After school, he went on to study physics at Oxford University. His first job was as an engineer for a telecommunications company. Following this, he spent a few months working at CERN (European Organisation for Nuclear Research) in Geneva, Switzerland. It was here in 1980 that Berners-Lee first proposed an idea that would lead to the Web.

His idea was to have a global network that would allow researchers around the world to share information. This would be done using 'Hypertext'; a computer language made up of a set of instructions and data. At this stage, the idea was still a proposal, and as with all scientific proposals, Berners-Lee needed to make a prototype. This was called ENQUIRE and was a simple hypertext program. It was to be the predecessor to the World Wide Web. It is worth remembering at this point that the 'Web' is not the Internet.

The Internet was first developed by the U.S. military. It was a worldwide communication network of computers that went live in 1969. Its purpose was to send information quickly between computers around the world. The World Wide Web is the part of the Internet that contains websites and webpages.

After working for a few years on a different project, Berners-Lee returned to CERN in 1984. In 1989, he published a paper – 'Information Management: A Proposal'. In this paper he proposed joining up hypertext with the Internet. The idea was to create a way of sharing and distributing information globally. The hypertext language was called HTML (HyperText Markup Language). HTML is the language that most webpages are written in. The world's very first webpage went online at CERN on August 6th, 1991. It contained information on the World Wide Web project.

Today, the World Wide Web is the most used service on the Internet. Sending emails is the second most used service. At the time of writing, in 2018, there were around 1.3 billion websites worldwide. There are close to 4 billion Internet users globally. In the history of invention and engineering there is probably nothing that has spread so widely and so quickly. It could be argued that of all the inventors and engineers that we have studied in this book, Tim Berners-Lee has had the greatest impact on our lives.

MEMO

Vocabulary

The underlined word appears in the text. Choose the word below which best matches the underlined word.

1) It was while consulting the map that Karl realized he was lost.
   a) looking at b) searching c) taking

2) To get the credit for doing something, you sometimes need some publicity.
   a) money b) recognition c) time

3) At this point, we only have a few members.
   a) place b) time c) age

4) Distributing consumer products around the world is a complex process.
   a) pushing b) understanding c) delivering

5) The meeting was to have a big impact on her life.
   a) influence b) moment c) idea

Understanding 1

Look at the reading passage and choose the correct expression.

1) The Web is so important that it now plays a ------- role in most of our lives.
   a) ubiquitous b) daily c) major

2) The plan that would ------- Berners-Lee to design the Web was conceived in Europe.
   a) lead b) take c) teach

3) The late 1960's saw the Internet go -------.
   a) live b) global c) wrong

4) Berners-Lee was interested in finding a way of s________________ information around the world.

5) Sending emails is a very popular ________________ on the Internet.

Understanding 2

Look at the reading passage again and decide if the following statements are true or false. Be ready to explain your choice.

1) T / F Many people were responsible for the creation of the World Wide Web.

2) T / F Berners-Lee did not really get into electronics until he was an adult.

3) T / F The idea of the World Wide Web was to let people in different countries share information.

4) T / F The Internet and the World Wide Web were both invented at the same time.

5) T / F In 2018, there were no less than one billion websites worldwide.

Dictation

31

Listen and fill in the blanks using the words below:

broke	person	success	female	access
uploaded	backstage	male	throughout	band
imagine	growing	break	bands	image

In 2014, around 1.8 billion digital images were being 1. ______________ every day. That number is almost certainly 2. ______________ every year. So many people now have 3. ______________ to a camera that around every two minutes, humans now take more photos than were taken 4. ______________ the entire 1800's. The very first photograph to be uploaded on the World Wide Web was actually of a rock 5. ______________. They were called *Les Horribles Cernettes*, an all-6. ______________, physics-themed group, founded in 1990 by a graphic designer who was working at CERN. The 7. ______________ who uploaded the 8. ______________ was none other than Tim Berners-Lee. He uploaded the 9. ______________ photo of the band in 1992. While the Web is still growing every day, the *Cernettes* 10. ______________ up in 2012.

Think about it

When computer scientists think about how different websites are connected to each other, they use something called **graph theory**. A graph is a set of **vertices** or **nodes** and a set of **edges**.
Look at this example of a simple graph:

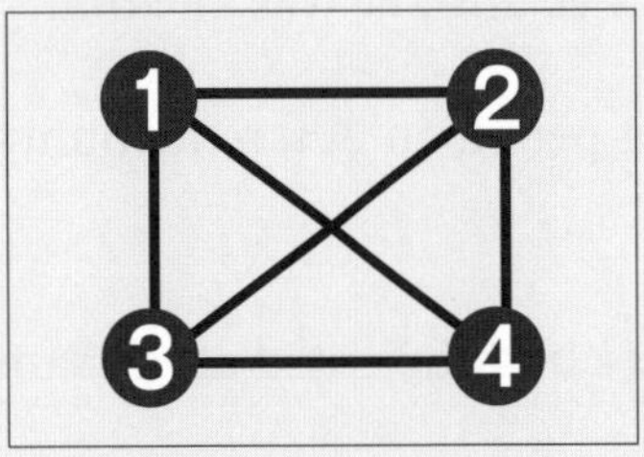

The **nodes** are (1,2,3,4).
The **edges** are {(1,2), (2,3), (3,4), (4,1), (1,3), (2,4)}

This is an **undirected graph**, so 1 connects to 2 and 2 connects to 1.
There are also **directed graphs**, which only go in one direction, and the **edges** have an arrow. Graphs can also be **weighted** or **unweighted**. In a **weighted graph**, each **edge** has a value or **cost**.

Draw the following weighted graph:

Nodes—(A,B,C,D,E)
Edges—{(A,C 12), (A,D 60), (B,A 10), (C,B 20), (C,D 32), (E,A 7)}

Now, imagine that the nodes in this weighted graph are buildings, the edges are streets and the costs are minutes. What is the quickest way to get from E to D?

Go to page 107 for a further activity.

Further 'Think About It' Questions

Further 'Think about it' question

Unit 1

Explain Archimedes' principle in your own words. How would you prove the theory?

Unit 2

Leonardo da Vinci's ornithopter was unsuccessful as a flying machine. Can you think why it is unlikely that a human-powered ornithopter would fly?

Can you think of any way that a human-powered ornithopter could fly, even for a few seconds?

Unit 3

The Industrial Revolution changed the world forever. Many of these changes were positive, but some were negative.

Think about the impacts of the Industrial Revolution on economics, technology, society and politics, and list as many positive and negative aspects as you can.

Here are two to get you started:

Positive	Negative
Technological Advancement	*Terrible working conditions*

MEMO

Unit 4

The Maglev train being built in Japan will take passengers from Tokyo to Nagoya at very high speeds. What kind of problems do you think the engineers building the line face?

Unit 5

What is the longest underwater tunnel in the world today? Can you think of any other locations in Japan or in other parts of the world where a long underwater tunnel could be built?

Unit 6

If you ride a motorbike that is a two-stroke, it will produce more power than one with a four-stroke engine. Why do you think this is?

MEMO

Unit 7

The Eiffel Tower was the tallest structure of its day. Since then, towers and buildings have gotten higher and higher, with the Burj Khalifa in Dubai, at 829.8 metres, being the world's tallest structure.

However, is there a limit to how high buildings can go? What needs to happen in the design if buildings are going to be super-tall? What lessons could we possibly learn from the Eiffel Tower?

Unit 8

Thomas Edison improved the light bulb to make it more practical and affordable. Think of a common object and try to think of ways to improve it.

Unit 9

Of the power generation sources used to create electricity around the world, over 50% are non-renewable.

Make a list of all the items, gadgets and appliances you use that in some way require electricity. If at some point in the future you were only able to use half of these things, which would you choose to keep? Give reasons for your answers.

MEMO

Unit 10

The Model T was a tough, durable little car that could even drive up mountains! Nowadays, however, there are many specific types of cars. List as many different types of cars as you can, and say what each type is designed for.

Unit 11

Marconi used Morse code for his wireless signals. The code is still used to this day, especially at sea. What are the advantages of using Morse code?

Unit 12

Because Alan Turing was able to break the Enigma code, it is said that World War II was shortened by up to two years. Turing therefore probably saved the lives of many thousands of people. Can you think of any other actions by individuals in history that have probably saved the lives of thousands, or even more, people?

MEMO

Unit 13

As a prominent female inventor, Stephanie Kwolek is quite unusual. Most of the famous inventors and engineers you will read about are men. According to UNESCO, as of 2017, the number of females studying STEM (Science, Technology, Engineering and Mathematics) subjects in higher education globally is only 35%. There are many reasons why fewer females than males study STEM topics. What do you think those reasons are? Also, do you think it is important that more girls choose to study STEM subjects? Give reasons for your answer.

Unit 14

The Apple iPhone is always being upgraded with new apps and features. If you were part of the Apple team, what features would you like to see on the next Apple iPhone? Give reasons for your choices.

Unit 15

The World Wide Web and the Internet have changed the lives of many people. Write a short essay (2-3 paragraphs) outlining what you think are the positives and negatives of the Internet.

MEMO

MEMO

MEMO

Eureka! [B-912]
—Great Discoveries and Achievements in Science, Engineering, and Technology—

世界を飛躍させた偉人たち —英語で学ぶ理工系の常識—

第1刷 2020年1月29日
第5刷 2024年3月29日

著　者 フィリップ・ザムレイ・グレアム Philip Zamrej Graham
ゴードン・A. リード Gordon A. Reid
田中武夫 Takeo Tanaka
澤田知香子 Chikako Sawada
松岡幹就 Mikinari Matsuoka
奥村直史 Naofumi Okumura

発行者 南雲一範 Kazunori Nagumo
発行所 株式会社 南雲堂
〒162-0801 東京都新宿区山吹町361
NAN'UN-DO Publishing Co., Ltd.
361 Yamabuki-cho, Shinjuku-ku, Tokyo 162-0801, Japan
振替口座：00160-0-46863
TEL: 03-3268-2311（営業部：学校関係）
03-3268-2384（営業部：書店関係）
03-3268-2387（編集部）
FAX: 03-3269-2486

編集者 丸小雅臣
組版・印刷 啓文堂
イラスト アヴェーレ 渡辺 恵
装　丁 アヴェーレ 渡辺 恵
検　印 省 略
コード ISBN978-4-523-17912-2 C0082

Printed in Japan
落丁・乱丁，その他不良品がございましたら，お取り替えいたします。

E-mail nanundo@post.email.ne.jp
URL https://www.nanun-do.co.jp/